Mommy, Teach me How to Read

Written by:
Harmel Deanne Codi, JD, MBA

Illustrated by:
Jewel Mason

Mommy Teach me How to Play

3

Marcus   Nina

DEDICATION

To my children,
Jewel and Jodari – my source of
inspiration and drive.

Jasmine and Clarence met in high school. After their graduation, Jasmine went to college across the State, and Clarence went to military college in another State.

8

Clarence always wanted to join the military like his Dad and his granddad. Clarence's Dad, Jerome, served and retired from the Navy.

Jerome Sr, his granddad, was a well-decorated Tuskegee Airmen who served in the military for nearly thirty years.

Jasmine, on the other hand, came from a family of educators. Her Dad was the town's elementary school principal, and her mom was a high school math teacher.

So, it was a big surprise when Jasmine met Clarence for the first time in high school, even though they lived in the same city all their lives.

After college, Clarence joined the military, and Jasmine became a school counselor.

They got married shortly after, and two years later, they had a twin boy and girl named Marcus and Nina.

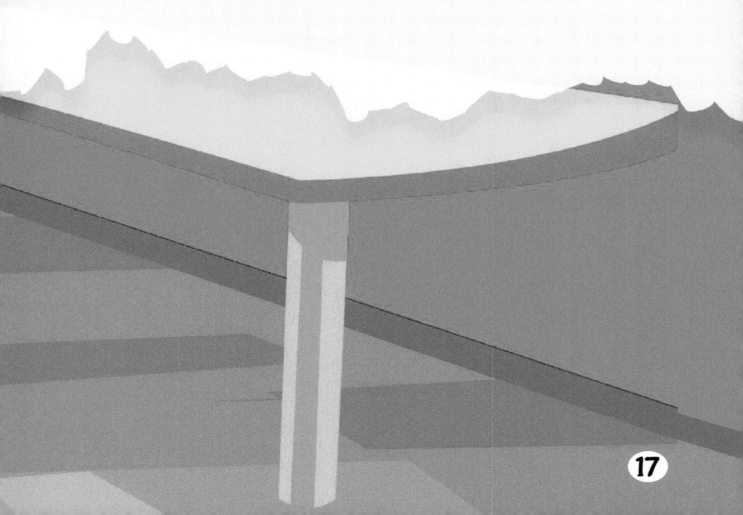

Marcus was quiet and observant, while Nina was lively and inquisitive.

Clarence and Jasmine love each other, and they love their two adorable children just the same.

A year after the twins were born, Clarence was deployed with the military. So, Jasmine stayed home to take care of the twins and their new puppy, Mumbo.

The twins grew fast, and before she could blink her eyes, they were two years old, then two and a half, and it was almost time to go to school.

The twins were smart, inquisitive, and precocious - they love to learn and learn everything fast. It is no wonder that they could not wait to start school.

So, their Mommy, Jasmine went to enroll them in the nearby Head Start program.

When she explained to the twins, Head Start is a school program you go to before you go to kindergarten. They protested.

"No!, Mommy, we want to go to kindergarten," Marcus debated

"Can you teach us how to read faster, please?" Replied Nina.

"Oh! My goodness," Mommy shouted with joy.

"I will do just that." She recanted excitedly.

22

The next day, Jasmine's sister, Auntie Jo, called, and Nina picked the phone. Auntie Jo said to Nina: "Your Mommy said that you and Marcus are learning how to read."

"Yes, we are starting kindergarten once we can read like Mommy," said Nina. Auntie Jo laughed. "You don't have much time, Nina," she exclaimed with laughter.

"I know, Auntie Jo. That's what we told Mommy," Nina argued. Auntie Jo said: "I am sending lots of books next week that you that you and Marcus can continue to practice." "Thank you, Auntie Jo," Nina uttered with a grin, then she handed the phone to her Mommy.

The twins were eager to start school and were very excited about that. Their conversations were all about school, reading, and what they would do when they got to school.

They often played "school" with each other, and when their friends visited, they pretended to be the teachers and students.

When they visited their grandparents, they wanted to show them their reading skills by reading everything around the house.

Their Dad, who is serving in the military overseas, would get an ear full when he would call home to talk to them.

They love telling their Dad about how they were getting ready to go to school and how Mommy was teaching them how to read before they start.

So, one Saturday afternoon shortly before school started, Jasmine took the twins to the store for school shopping.

Once at the store, they started looking around. "Mommy, may I have this for school?" Nina asked as she runs towards a doll.

"No, Nina, you don't need that for school. We just need to buy you a school bag, a notebook, and crayons," Mommy said, smiling.

"Can you buy us a new storybook too? We love it when you read us stories, Mommy." Marcus said as they walked around the store. Mommy nodded, and the twins were thrilled.

Later that evening, after they were ready for bed, Nina asked, "Mommy, will you read the new storybook you bought for us?

Mommy took the book and read it out loud. The story was about a prince who bravely saved a beautiful princess from her captors. And they lived happily ever after.

The twins really enjoyed it. "I wish I could read fast like you," Marcus said, with a sad face. Nina felt the same way too.

"Once you start school, you will get better and better," Mommy said, kissing them good night.

"I can't wait to start school so I can read books myself!" Nina whispered, and Marcus nodded.

The next day after lunchtime, when Nina and Marcus played in the living room, they brought out their alphabet blocks.

46

Their mom heard them singing the alphabet song, pointing to the blocks and sounding words. "We can do this, Nina," Marcus said. When Mommy heard that, she smiled and joined them.

48

"I'm so proud of you two. You know your alphabet so well. We will read a special book at bedtime tonight, and I promise it will be exceptional," Mommy said. The twins were so excited.

Mommy had all the best books, and they loved to hear how she read them. They couldn't wait to learn. "Yeah! "They screamed and ran around the living room, excitedly.

At bedtime, after they brushed their teeth, their Mommy walked into their room with a brand new book. They had not seen that book before. The book did not have any pictures nor words.

"It is blank," blurted Nina. They looked at each other confused.

"How are we going to read this book? There are no words,"

Marcus asked, opening the book.

"Oh, Marcus, just wait. This is very special," Mommy said.

She turned off the lights, and just like magic, the book's words started to glow in the dark. "Wow! This is so cool. Nina and Marcus shouted in excitement.

This is like learning to read. When you are small and just starting out, everything looks blank in your eyes, but after you learn how to read, you will see all the words clearly," Mommy said with a big smile.

As their Mommy read the magical book, she asked them to point out letters in the alphabet. This was the best story Nina and Marcus had ever heard. They now understood how reading works, and they were happy to learn slowly.

About this Project

We are sincerely grateful that you choose to read our books to your child. It is an honor to bring this book series to the world and that all children will have more access to age-appropriate books to enjoy. This project was a long time coming, and we are thankful for all the support that undergird its arrival.

Early literacy is so critical in the lives of all children. The earlier children learn to read, brighter is their future. We hope that you continue to read for the child in your life as early as in utero. When we make reading and learning fun for kids, it becomes a wonderful hobby that opens a world of imagination and adventure.

We are so excited to bring this reading opportunity to all children, which is why all profits from our books' purchase go to our non-profit organization to encourage early literacy. We donate thousands of books yearly to our local pre-k and kindergarteners through our ¨My First Book Project.¨ Your purchase opens access to donation of more books to children in our community that they too, can learn to read early. After all, we believe all readers are leaders

For more information on our non-profits and the community engagements, please visit: www.communityalliances.net

About the story line:

These books' ideas came to me while I was pregnant with my daughter Jewel (this book's illustrator) almost two decades ago. With both of my children, I started reading and singing for Jewel and my son Jodari once I discovered that I was pregnant. I knew that this would be the best gift that I could give them to propel them to a bright future as they become students and beyond. The years come quicker than I expected, and despite best efforts, I could not find time to get the books published. Then the pandemic happens, and we were all at home simultaneously, then Jewel and I started working on this project. Who would imagine that the books that were intended for them would be a gift to all children?

It has been an incredible journey to recreate these characters and bring these stories to our young readers. I am so grateful to my family that has partly inspired me to make this project a reality, and to each person who nudged me into embarking on this new endeavor. It has been a real joy.

About the Series
If you enjoy this book, please explore the entire series:
Mommy! Teach me how to read

Mommy! Teach me How to Count

Mommy! Teach me How to Sing

Mommy! Teach me How to Play

Mommy! Teach me How to Write

Mommy! Teach me How to Pray

Mommy! Teach me How to Dance

Daddy is home from Military

Daddy , Teach me how to ride Bicycle

Daddy, Teach me how to swim

Daddy , Teach me how to tie my shoelace

Lightning Source UK Ltd.
Milton Keynes UK
UKHW052106211120
373771UK00002B/119

9 781735 975924